THE
SECRET
VALLEY

THE
SECRET
VALLEY
THE REAL ROMANCE OF
UNCONQUERED LAKELAND

BY
NICHOLAS SIZE
WITH A FOREWORD BY
SIR HUGH WALPOLE

"Truth is stranger than fiction"
- and one helps the other.

First published in 1930.
Reprint of the seventh edition
Llanerch Publishers, Felinfach, 1996.

ISBN 1 86143 011 6

*The publishers have made every effort to trace the representatives
of the estate, without success. Those concerned are invited to write
to Llanerch Publishers, Felinfach, Lampeter, Dyfed, SA48 8PJ.

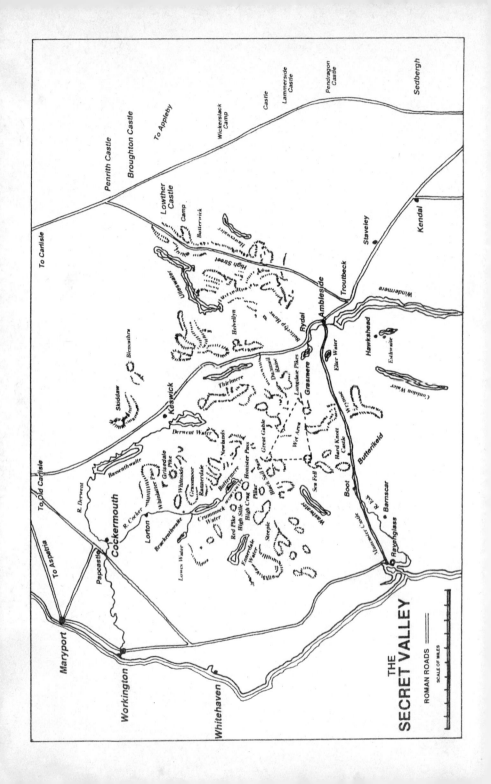

THE
SECRET VALLEY

ROMAN ROADS

SCALE OF MILES

CONTENTS

CHAPTER
PAGE

A note to the 1996 reprint:

NICHOLAS SIZE, 1867 - 1953.

Nicholas Size came to the Victoria Hotel, Buttermere (now the Bridge Hotel) in 1928 from Bradford, where he had worked as a railway goods manager. The move to an hotel in the heart of one of Lakeland's finest valleys was the realisation of an ambition he had cherished for many years.

He had ideas of promoting the quiet, remote hamlet into a flourishing tourist centre. Fortunately, plans for a beer garden and a chair-lift to the top of a neighbouring fell did not materialise; a golf course near the hotel had only a very short life.

He was keen on walking the hills and fought battles with local landowners in support of the right to roam. He knew a great deal about the valley, its people and its past but his published work owes most to his imagination.

Something of a maverick, he had a sharp eye for business and was by no means universally popular. A compulsive raconteur, he regaled his guests at length with yarns and anecdotes - an imposition not always welcome after a day's walking and a hearty dinner.

"Auld Nick", an eccentric to the last, is buried not in a country churchyard but in a lonely grave on the fell near his hotel. He even composed his own epitaph, a self-assessment that, it would seem, was not shared by all his acquaintances:

No tombstone will ornament my grave,
No over confidence about salvation,
Write me down one that loved his fellowmen
And was a credit to his generation.

George Bott, 1995.

FOREWORD TO THE FIRST EDITION

This little book needs no foreword of mine or anyone else's. It is clear enough for its plan and its purpose. But I hope that I may be allowed an opportunity here of saying that I think that Mr. Size has succeeded in a very difficult task.

It is not for me to say whether or no his history is accurate. In history I have always considered the spirit of the law more than the letter; farther than that, Mr Collingwood is, I think, the only man alive who has knowledge enough both of the place and the period to say with authority whether Mr. Size is to be believed. (W. G. Collingwood died October 1932 - ed.) For myself I *am* a believer because the atmosphere is here.

How many prose works have captured the mysterious atmosphere of these lakes and hills? Very few. In our own time, "Thorstein of the Mere" first and foremost. After that -- well, it is not easy to summon them to the eye, although I would like to put in a word for one of the finest of all North Country novels -- Mrs. Ward's "Helbeck of Bannisdale".

This book of Mr. Size's has somewhere in its heart an authentic core. His English is simple but in its directness most honest and effective. His pictures are vivid: his figures human. But none of these things gives the key to the fascination of this little book. The key rests, I fancy, in the love of the author for the country of which he is writing, and most fortunately that love has not led to sentiment or gush.

Mr. Size writes like a man, and like a man of his

hands. Nothing is more difficult, as the writer of this little foreword knows to his cost, than the recovery of past history in a place that is alive for you in every stone, in every shadowed hill, in every tumbling stream. What you must do, if your work is to be of any value, is to use your imaginative eye, and yet not be false to your known facts.

Mr. Size has the advantage of me in his facts. I have not knowledge enough to challenge him, nor do I wish to. But I also love the county that he loves and am sensitive to any falsity in the conception of it. There is no falsity of imagination here: this is an honest book.

I hope that for the sake of the valley with which it deals it continues to win a host of friends.

HUGH WALPOLE.

THE SECRET VALLEY

CHAPTER I

INTRODUCTORY

The years which followed 1066 raised Lakeland to a position of great importance. It became the haven of miserable refugees who fled in hundreds of thousands from the savage Norman devastation of Yorkshire and Lancashire, and for almost a century maintained a guerilla warfare which cost the Normans one army after another, until the dread and mysterious mountains of Cumberland came to be regarded with horror by the invaders.

The broad fact that our local men kept Lakeland out of Doomsday Book is perhaps their greatest monument, and though the Norman monks and bookmen refused to chronicle the repeated successes of heroes fighting for their homes, whom they regarded as most wicked rebels against the King's Majesty, there is sufficient evidence in our local place-names, old ruins, and half-forgotten stories, to reconstruct the most outstanding features of the great struggle---which in itself was an epic of the English race.

These half-forgotten stories belong to families like the Harrisons, or to localities like Ambleside and Buttermere; they have no assignable authors, but seem to spring from the hearts of whole peoples and many generations. The modern movements and intermixture of the people, however, is killing all the old traditions; and unless we gather them up and get them into print, we shall soon have nothing left but the dry bones of history; which in its abbreviated form repels our young people, instead of attracting them to enjoy and appreciate the wonderful story of our race.

Truth is stranger than fiction, and according to the greatest modern historians the position of Lakeland in Norman times was highly interesting and almost unbelievable. The following quotations from that monumental work, *The Victoria History of Cumberland and Westmorland,* will show that there is much justification for such research as mine, and for the piecing together of old wive's tales which may well be true.

Thus says the history:---"It is one of the most singular eccentricities of territorial conquest that a small corner of ancient Cumbria could be held without title or grant for more than half a century after it had been absorbed into the English Kingdom". (Page 306.) "A mantle of silence, like the veil of Isis, hangs over it till the close of the eleventh century. Doomsday Book has nothing to tell us". (*Page* 296.)

Here we have a reliable starting point; the Norman tax-gatherers, who sat in the Chapter House at Gloucester, near the great pillars which William and Matilda his Queen were erecting to the glory of God and the astonishment of the English in 1086, had to leave out the details of two of the fairest of our English counties; and could only maintain "a mantle of silence like the veil of Isis" about the appalling losses in men and money continuing year after year in the endeavour to subdue them.

Even the veil of Isis, however, has corners which can be raised; and among the invigorating heights and valleys of the most beautiful scenes in England you may see some of the faint traces of Earl Boethar's glorious and prolonged defence; and even visit the inaccessible and secret valley, which was the heart and arsenal of that army of men and women of our own race, who long ago fought the Normans to a standstill.

Is it nothing to us that the fathers of our branch of the race succeeded where Hereward, the son of Lady Godiva, failed, and that we entered the realm peacefully and by consent in the reign of Henry II --- unconquered and on favourable terms? It was even agreed that the men of Cumberland and Westmorland should be immune from military service beyond their own frontiers, and that their main obligation should consist of the safe convoying of the

King's army through the two counties when going to or from Scotland. *(Victoria History, ii, page 251.)*

CHAPTER II

THE REFUGEES

After the conquest of the greater part of England there were rebellions in the North, and the people of Yorkshire and Lancashire gave the King so much trouble that he wreaked his vengeance upon them, and turned their land into a great desert, whilst the inhabitants had no choice but to flee or be killed.

The Aethling Edgar, heir to King Edward's throne, was in the South with his two sisters, Margaret and Christina; they all fled to Dunfermline by sea, where the first named had the good fortune to marry the Scottish King, Malcolm Canmore, who, in the general scramble, occupied as much new territory as possible, and counted it a fair dowry for his English wife. The loyalty of her northern countrymen followed Queen Margaret, and many thousands changed their nationality from English to Scottish, glad to throw off a dangerous allegiance and adopt one which might provide some degree of safety.

A large section of the refugees, however, turned aside towards the mountains of Lakeland, and their tales of wanton murder, cruelty and pillage ensured a warm welcome from the half-Norwegian inhabitants, among whom hospitality had been a religion ever since the days when Father Odin was the chief of the gods. The old pagan religion had long been dead, but it was a kindly one, and those who loved it were a kindly people. Even to this day the youngest of them half believe that at Yuletide, the ancient deity, with his long white beard and sack of gifts, comes from Norway in a reindeer sledge and drives down the chimney to bring each child his heart's desire. Among the kindly, hospitable people, the host would starve rather than that the guest should suffer, but as time went on all starved alike.

Many of the refugees brought their valuables on pack horses, their swine and the remnants of their flocks and herds; but many among them were broken men and women, desperate with their losses, and thankful for any respite from the Norman butchery, which spared neither the young children who would soon have been the backbone of the nation, nor the aged, who, for the sake of peace, were only too willing to accept the new dominance.

The flood of refugees who came to Lakeland soon produced a famine, and though the lakes and rivers yielded wonderful quantities of salmon in their season, it was a poor country for grain. Convoys of provisions, however, passed frequently from the South to Carlisle, and whenever possible they were pillaged by the starving people.

King William himself made a royal progress in 1072, and left his great lieutenant Ranulf Meschin in charge. To him and his brother William all the land was given between the Rerecross of Stainmore, Morecambe Bay, and the crossing into Scotland at the head of the Solway; so that these two became almost the greatest of the Conqueror's nobles in the North of England. (Tower Miscellaneous Rolls, No. 459/3, *Victoria History*, p. 297. The name Meschin or Le Meschin means junior, or the junior branch of a family).

The northern part of this delightful country belonged to the Northumbrian Earl Gospatric, who thought he had made himself secure by buying the earldom of Carlisle from King William soon after 1066. The King, however, distrusted him, and the main object of the large army he took to Carlisle in 1072 was to turn out Gospatric, and replace him with the brothers Ranulf and William Meschin, the younger branch of the great Norman family. Large and continuous reinforcements were provided to set these two noblemen upon their feet; and throughout the lifetime of the King the vicissitudes of these two armies were probably the greatest of the strains which his administration had to bear.

William Meschin was given the rich country of Copeland, which lies between the mountains and the sea, and as the years went on he slowly established himself by virtue of the superior armament of his forces, and the generalship and methods which had been so successful further South. Armies, however, take a great deal of feeding, and those in Cumberland were not able to live upon the country because everything possible was taken up to the refugees among the lakes and mountains. Thus it happened that particularly large convoys of food were required, and as these were pushed up from the South to Carlisle they were eagerly waited for by the refugees, and a great many of them were captured and disappeared.

They, of course, travelled through the difficult country for which Ranulf Meschin was responsible, and as he had to guard his brother's convoys as well as his own it is obvious that their protection must have hampered his other activities.

From a broad view of this long-drawn-out portion of the campaign, it is apparent that in a dozen years he slowly fortified the valley of the Eden with endless castles, stockades, and camps, of which a dozen were rebuilt in the Plantagenet period and still remain. People, however, have forgotten why they were first built, and how the starving refugees, led by the grim Norsemen of the mountains, came down into the valleys both from the East and West full of desperation and ready to attack even the largest guard.

Nowadays two great main lines of railway pass from the South through the Eden Valley to Carlisle, but in Ranulf's time there were only unpaved tracks and a Roman road or two, with bogs and marshes on either side, which local people passed over with impunity, whilst the Normans, with their heavier equipment and ignorance of the causeways, seldom returned if they ventured on a pursuit.

On the one side these marshes stretched beyond Hartside and Crossfell to the country south of Alston; they were famous for swallowing up men and horses, and were looked upon as hopeless; but on the western side more inexplicable things happened. The mysterious mountains, the very size of which seemed to vary (for in cloudy weather all mountains seem higher than when they are under a blue sky), were said to be the homes of demons and giants, and the superstitious soldiery from the flat plains of France were demoralised by the unfamiliar conditions; they feared the winds which buffeted them like a giant's arm and threw down horse and man, the mists which moved about and were sometimes found to be full of enemies, and the curious awesomeness of the shafts of light or of darkness, which were never still, and seemed to presage death. It was an evil land of enchantment, in which the real and the unreal were confused together, where death came silently, and even the bodies vanished. Wolves they could understand, and men they were not afraid of, but devils and the devil's own country, with witches and warlocks howling at night, and whole detachments of men suddenly disappearing without leaving a trace behind --- it was more than they were prepared to go on with.

They called his Majesty William the Bastard, instead of King, and where it was safe to desert, they deserted. Reinforcements told them how comfortable the Normans were making themselves in the South; but here, with food unreliable, arrows which seemed to come from nowhere, and insecurity enough to give the "horrors" every night, the bravery which was born of their superior armament oozed away, and panic spread at every hint of the supernatural, so that nothing was successful.

Ranulf himself was, of course, above these fears --- and whilst holding the Roman roads in the valley of the Lune and the Grayrigg track from Kendal to Tebay, he worked West towards Haweswater where (at an entrenched fortification raised by Earl Boethar and now called Butterwick) he had located an English headquarters or base of supplies. Beyond this he knew of a Roman road which he hoped would be as useful to him as those in the Eden Valley, and he did his best to capture it; but soon he found that all military operations in this direction were very expensive; his army melted away faster than he could get reinforcements; he could obtain no tangible success, and found that his royal master was a hard man when he was dissatisfied.

Other Norman lords who were sent to report damned him with faint praise, and counselled a great attack from Kendal towards Ambleside, which he had felt himself too weak to undertake. With driblets of reinforcements and the withdrawal of the men from Butterwick which he had meantime captured, he concentrated on Kendal, and at the last moment "took a risk", and withdrew the large section of his men from the all-important work of keeping the Carlisle route open. This turned out badly, for his opponents got to hear of it, and a large force under Ari Knudson overwhelmed several weak garrisons and captured all the provisions then in transit; whereat there was bitter complaint from both Carlisle and Copeland.

The attack from Kendal to Ambleside was only temporarily successful, as the English enemy put men across lake Windermere in the darkness, who cut Ranulf's communications and held their post until large forces were sent back to dislodge them; whereupon they took to the lake and got across in safety, as they had boats and rafts while the Normans had none.

Ranulf was pleased with Ambleside itself when he captured it, as the Roman *castrum* was very strong; and as it was at the junction of the roads westward to Ravenglass and northwards towards Penrith, he felt that with adequate reinforcements he could control the country exactly as the Romans had done long ago. To do this, however, it was clear that he would require another army, and as the events turned out it was impossible to get it. The King was preoccupied in Normandy, and Ranulf was at last obliged to withdraw from Ambleside and use all his army in keeping open the route to Carlisle, which Earl Boethar had completely closed for a period, so that Dolfin Gospatricson, with Scottish assistance, had captured the city.

At different times, Ranulf Meschin had obtained information from prisoners under torture about his opponents, and had learned that they obeyed an Earl or Jarl called Boethar, who lived in a secret valley which none has seen.

It was clearly nowhere near Ambleside (where indeed he had expected to find it); and curiously enough it had no name, though men sometimes called it "Little Norway". It was said to be up in the clouds among the mountain tops, and was always described as far away from everywhere. It puzzled Ranulf, for nobody ever admitted having seen it, and the routes to it were unknown. Yet in it there was clearly a controlling intelligence thwarting him, and signalling with lights at night from one horrid mountain top to another; rightly he divined that it was in this secret valley he should find the head of the organisation which was fighting him.

Let us therefore look at the other side of the picture, while King William dies in Normandy, and Ranulf vainly pleads for reinforcements to enable him to push on from Kendal.

CHAPTER III

THE NORSEMEN

Since before 876, when the Norwegians and Danes under Halfdan fought with the peaceful Angles and burnt their city of Carlisle over their heads, there had been a trading colony near Ravenglass.

The Norsemen used what was left of the old Roman port and also built a city of their own further north, which they called Barnscar. They traded peacefully with the Cumbrian Welsh, who found them useful neighbours. The Isle of Man, forty miles away, was their great shipping centre; and a good trade was done in arms and metalwork, as well as all the products of Ireland, Scotland and Wales, for the Norsemen had a monopoly of the carrying trade of the Irish Sea.

In 890 their numbers were largely increased, as their own King, Harald Harfager, who looked upon them as rebels, made a descent upon the Isle of Man; whereupon the colony there scattered, and many settled along the coasts of Cumberland and Lancashire, and did an increasing trade.

The Cumbrians were, of course, Romanized Britons, with all the needs of civilized people: commerce was very necessary to them, and as they had no taste for seafaring themselves, they became

15

good customers to the Norsemen. About 937, however, their king died --- and it was an unfortunate
time to make a change of rulers, because a clash
was impending between the Saxon king, Athelstan,
and all the Danes, Noresmen, Welsh, Scottish, and
Irish to the north and west of his kingdom.

The new Cumbrian king was Dunmail, whose
only monument today is a heap of stones called
Dunmail Raise, between Grassmere and Thirlmere
--- a heap which is a warning to every motorist who
passes, for Dunmail wrecked his people, and pos-
terity only remembered him as a fool. He was a
great blustering man, boastful of his kingdom of
Strathclyde and Cumbria, boastful of his Royal
relatives, King Constantine of Scotland and others,
overbearing in council, intemperate concerning liq-
uor and food, tremendous in his own importance,
and a great hunter.

In the year of his accession he failed his friends,
and remained neutral instead of marching into
Cheshire to help them at Brunanburgh. Then, instead of taking advantage of his luck in not being
involved in this defeat, and making friends with his
overlord, King Athelstan, he repudiated the oath
made by his predecessor, and practically rebelled
without actually doing so. Athelstan died three
years after Brunanburgh, but his brother, Edmund
the Magnificent, pressed Dunmail so strongly that

16

he could find no middle course, and finally tried to throw off the Saxon Yoke.

Thus it happened that Edmund invaded Cumbria with an army so large that he was able to divide it, sending one portion along Thirlmere and the other by Grassmere and Rydal. They drove King Dunmail out of his city near Wythburn, and signally defeated him at the point where the heap of stones is lying on the roadside. The defeat was so complete that Edmund demanded the Royal regalia and the exile of the King, with other terms which have been forgotten. The sons of Dunmail, however, took the crown and other emblems of power, and cast them into Grisedale Tarn, thus cheating the Saxon king out of one of the visible signs of his victory. For this defiance he had their eyes put out, and was more harsh than would otherwise have been the case.

Dunmail now involved the whole of Cumbria in his ruin; he made some sort of an arrangement with the Prince of North wales (who wanted men for his frontiers), and marched all his army, and such women as would go, all the way from Cumbria to the Vale of Clwydd, where their descendants (heavy, dark men) can still be traced --- though successive wars sadly reduced their numbers. Thus it came about that the valleys of Cumbria were depopulated in 945, and the Norwegian traders on the coast arranged for the immigration of many of their brethren from Norway.

These were young farmers from Tellmarken and Hardanger (land of hunger or poverty). They found Cumberland a splendid country and made it their own, renaming the mountains and villages, improving the farming, marrying such Welsh women as had remained behind, and leaving a far greater mark upon the country than its original Welsh inhabitants.

These latter found themselves in the forefront of every battle on the Welsh Marches, so that they have become almost exterminated. King Dunmail himself lived for a time in Wales, but as his influence diminished and his folly became more and more apparent, he decided to make the pilgrimage to Rome, where he might still call himself a king. The journey was, however, a hard one in those days, and somewhere between La Turbie and Eze, within sight of the blue Mediterranean, he was robbed and maltreated by the Saracens, who had captured those rocky villages; and there he left his bones and his troubles forever.

The Norsemen seem to have brought their sheep, a small black breed, with wool which made waterproofs, but which is now less valuable through mistaken efforts to breed it white. The animals are wonderfully hardy, and the lambs are very pretty.

They are generally born darker than their mothers, and become whiter as they grow older.

To return, however, to our story. The Norsemen who now owned the Lake District, fearing a repetition of the Saxon attack which had driven out Dunmail, sent an invitation to the great Norwegian soldier, Olaf Tryggvesson, to come and advise them about the defence of their country. He was a picturesque figure, who had once visited the Solway with fire and sword, but was now the husband of Lady Gyda of Wirral; and his fame had spread far and wide because of the brilliant way he had dealt with a dozen duels, to which he was challenged on the day when his lady chose him for her husband.

(Gyda, the sister of Olaf Quaran, King of Dublin, and daughter of Aulaf who was defeated by King Athelstan at Brunanburgh, was widow of the Earl of Wirral, Flintshire, and South-West Lancashire. She boldly chose King Olaf at a council which had been called to dispose of her hand, and all the other suitors challenged him to a series of duels in consequence, but he outgeneralled and wounded them all. --- *Heimskringla*).

She was a king's daughter, and about 990, came with her husband to find some plan of defence for her countrymen in Cumberland and Westmorland. Barnscar was incapable of being made into a safe refuge; but from the top of Gavel, which is the centre of everything (and which we call Great Gable), they saw a valley which was almost impregnable, and which they fixed upon as a secret rendezvous for all the people. Its best means of access was by boat along a twisting lake, and as it was out of sight from almost every point of view, and was easy of defence, they prepared it for its destiny. At the foot of Crummock Water they built a fortification to act as a depôt in the marshes, and arranged that there should always be boats to convey food, etc., up to the secret valley beyond the bend of the lake. The ground plan of this fortification still exists, and its oblong shape proves it to have been planned by a Norseman.

The attack for which this refuge was prepared never took place, but before a hundred years had passed another foe had taken the place of the sturdy Saxon, and the secret valley, withstanding all attacks, saved the lives of Norse and English alike from the exterminating ideas of the Normans.

In 990 the ruler of the colony was Doka of Eskdale, who was Godi or priest, and Sysman or sheriff, of all Lakeland. He favoured the enlargement of the old Roman castle on Hardknott Pass and resided nearby at a place which is now called Butterikeld. When Olaf visited him and weighed up all the possibilities the idea was given up.

As this place was on the Roman road to Am-

HARDKNOTT PASS WITH WALL OF ROMAN FORT (Cumbria Tourist Board)

bleside it was a valuable strategic point, but it could never become a sanctuary to which the whole colony could retreat in time of trouble, like the valley twelve miles away, which after a search through all Lakeland was finally pitched upon. This was ideal for its purpose, surrounded by high mountains; the passes by which they could be crossed were particularly dangerous, and the only safe and easy access was by means of boats on Crummock Water.

Although this sanctuary was hidden out of sight, its central position made it near to every part of the Lake District; and food for the thousands which it might accommodate could come in from any side, along paths which would be death-traps to a hostile army.

About 1070 this secret valley was adopted as his main centre by Boethar the Younger, a descendant of King Olaf's friend and an experienced soldier. In his youth he seems to have learned the art of war in Pembrokeshire, where the Norwegian colony of Haverford and Tenby was perpetually fighting for its life against the Welsh, and to this day there is a hill called after him in memory of some long-forgotten exploit.

By 1070, however, he had married a great lady and had settled down to rule in his own country. Thus it happened that when the flood of refugees broke upon Lakeland there was a capable and energetic ruler ready to do whatever was best; and the outlying farmers, eaten out of house and home by the fugitives, got good help and direction, as well as encouragement, instead of being left to become embittered against the poor desperate strangers.

Among the mountains hospitality is an older and deeper religion than any other, and the young Earl, with his rich wife, at first saw only a strengthening of their earldom; but afterwards the feeling of indignation against the Normans swallowed up everything else; and though the cause of Edward the Confessor's subjects, the priest-ridden Saxons in England, evoked no enthusiasm, the ill-usage of the free Danes and Norsemen who were now his guests called aloud for vengeance.

Many of the refugees brought strings of ponies laden with treasures or household stuff, and there were flocks and herds, but no carts, because there were practically no roads. Later on the ragged and starving fugitives brought no more than a pack strapped to their shoulders, and many died by the wayside leaving their children to struggle on towards the mountains.

Thousands of these refugees were shipped away from Ravenglass to the Isle of Man or Galloway, and all the local silver and the money or treasure that could be spared was brought back to feed the rest. The able-bodied men were armed and organised into bands, to plunder the Norman convoys of provisions passing towards Carlisle, and the women learned to grow rye and oats on virgin land, to help the wounded, and to make arrows for the men.

Rich and poor worked hand in hand, sleeping among the bracken in dry weather and in rough shelters in Winter, becoming stronger and more healthy as the open-air life benefited them.

Thus it happened that the place of refuge prepared by the sagacity of Olaf Tryggvesson, the greatest soldier of his time, as a safe sanctuary in case the Norwegians should be attacked and driven from their trading city of Barnscar, became the camp and nerve centre in a far greater war, in which a large section of the northern English were threatened with extermination.

Barnscar lay near the Irt, and one can realise the anxiety of its inhabitants concerning its defencelessness, and their invitation to the man who was afterwards the great King Olaf to come and advise them. His visit to Lakeland with his brave wife Gyda took place soon after their marriage; and they came down to this more beautiful edition of dear old Norway, and constructed the fortification at the foot of Crummock Water.

From this depôt boats could ply along the lake to the impregnable valley beyond Rannerdale Point, and everything would at once be done to provide a

23

wooden manor house and village, and to strengthen the natural defences; for the great Olaf was no procrastinator, and all he did both in England and Norway was done speedily and well. He turned Norway into a Christian country, and yet died at the age of thirty-five, after conquering two nations.

CHAPTER IV

GUERILLA WARFARE

The war went on year after year with continuous raids against the Norman convoys as they passed up Lonsdale and down the Eden Valley. There were heavy English losses, but they could easily be borne, and there were many wonderful successes, as the Normans were fighting in country which did not suit them. Armour for man and horse and knightly weapons were constantly being exported from Ravenglass to buy food, and help came in from Scotland and Ireland, where freedom had many friends and the Normans many enemies.

The secret valley was found to be a splendid centre. It already had a water-mill and bakery to take the place of the old hand-mills or querns used elsewhere. Also the Earl rebuilt the great wooden manor house, and organised a signalling service from the shoulder of the mountain Robinson, which in those days was called Robeacon, an awkward word to pronounce.

The paths up this mountain were widened and improved (as can be seen today), and though the Earl and his lieutenants, young Ackin and old Ari, were nearly always away fighting, everybody kept in touch with Buttermere.

The non-success of Ranulf Earl of Carlisle cost him his Court favour, and the constant raids which were made upon the convoys brought him bitter complaints from his august master. He held his position mainly because nobody else coveted it, and as his camps were constantly being captured and hardly a day passed without some ambuscade, he had many a sorry report to send to London.

In modern days the fell races at Grassmere and elsewhere provide wonderful exhibitions of the speed at which the dalesmen can run up or down a mountain, and we may be sure that in the ancient fighting, greater efforts were made; and places which the Normans could hardly climb at all gave safe and easy passage to the local men, so that small detachments of Normans were massacred whenever they ventured away from safety. Every twist of a mountain torrent, every patch of vegetation, either low down or high up, was likely to conceal a band of well-armed men, hard fighters, who all had some personal loss to avenge, and therefore it is not surprising that Earl Boethar's followers had many successes.

In the matter of archery the Normans were also at a disadvantage; their leaders favoured the short bows which afterwards developed into the crossbow, and which did not project an arrow either so far or so accurately as the long-bow which was afterwards adopted.

Earl Boethar's archery developed rapidly in the opposite direction. He himself had brought back the idea of the long yew bow from Pembrokeshire, and everybody made experiments. There is nothing like a war for teaching men to improve their weapons, and soon the long and heavy bows of the English, clumsy as they might look, were projecting arrows twice as far as before. Thus the Normans had good reason to be afraid of keen arrows coming apparently from nowhere, and taking toll before the presence of an enemy was suspected, and as they were a superstitious people who believed in many kinds of enchantment, the moral effect of their fellows' mysterious disappearances was probably considerable.

Their own bows were capable of more rapid archery, and this looked like an advantage, but as they were not often engaged in a pitched battle they seldom got any benefit from it.

In old Ari Knudson, Boethar had an able deputy in the convoy fighting, and as he sometimes crossed into the wild country between Brough and Alston (where Boethar had his greatest silver mine), and organised raids in unexpected places, his reputation was a wide one. Another great fighter was Boethar's younger brother Ackin, called for some reason "the well-beloved", but how he got this title

I do not know.

The fame of these two men is not yet dead, for people still use the phrase "Fighting like old Harry", and his name crops up in a hundred ways. We have quite dropped the Danish and Icelandic "Ari" which preceded the present form of the name, and which was in use in the eleventh century; but to this day there is no name more English than Harry or Ari, nor is there any name pleasanter to the ear.

The memory of Ackin, the Earl's brother, is less widespread. His home or burial place figures upon the Ordnance Map, but nothing is remembered of him except that he was well-beloved. He was carried up to his howe, and laid at rest by loving friends, near the spot which he had made his lookout station. Perhaps there were many sore hearts and many tears, but every detail has been long forgotten. Was he a courteous and considerate young man well beloved of women; or a good sportsman and dashing leader well beloved of men; or was he something more, as might befit a man beloved by the stricken and the war-worn, the widow and the orphan? Such, I am convinced, was this Ackin, or Haakon, who lost his life in Rannerdale eight hundred years ago; for though he must have been a splendid soldier, and a wise and resourceful leader, the title which he earned would be for very different qualities, perhaps for some wonderful large-heartedness, some greater depth of love and kindness than other men --- perhaps some skill in medicine or helpfulness. He was surely the man to whom all took their joys and sorrows, secure in his love and counsel, for love begets love, and certainly here was one who, above all things, loved his fellow-men.

An interesting feature of all the fighting was the provision of the "garments of invisibility" formerly used by Norwegian priests. These consisted of loose cloaks made of old rags of the same colour as the surrounding stones; and they enabled their wearers slowly to steal forward into positions which enabled them to kill their enemies in comparative safety.

Small wonder that the natives were called magicians, and that their mountains, which in cloudy weather looked taller than under a blue sky, got a name for evil enchantments.

Both young Ackin and old Ari were very successful in this kind of fighting, and as their men could shoot a hundred yards further than the Normans, as well as wield a deadly battle-axe or sword, it is not surprising that they were looked upon as wizards for whom burning would be too good.

CHAPTER V

BOETHAR'S MILL

Meanwhile William le Meschin, brother of the more arrogant and magnificent Ranulf, had a great deal of success in Copeland. The flat lands of North and West Cumberland were populated by that great pacific race the Angles, who, like our modern Quakers, were never ready to take up the sword, and believed it would be as easy to serve one master as another.

Like the Southern Angles of Norfolk and Suffolk they were governed by an Earl; and in 1066 this was Gospatric, who lived near the place now called Aspatria, and who had offered tribute to the Conqueror for his earldom of Carlisle and part of Northumberland, an offer which was first accepted and then rejected; so that Gospatric and his son Dolfin fled into Scotland to be heard of later, when Dolfin recaptured his father's city.

The Angles are among the most interesting and important of our ancestors, for their policy of peaceful penetration was so successful that the larger half of the island came to be called England after them; and it was their language, and not that of the Saxons, Danes, or Britons, which was adopted by the whole group. Also it is the Angles' idea of fair play, and "truth before every-thing", which

31

have distinguished us among the other peoples of the world. They were originally a priestly clan, teaching the religion of Father Odin, and it is a fact that their descendants have invented more religions than all the other nations put together, for are not the Americans as well as ourselves particularly proficient in this matter?

The British Israelites claim the Angles as one of the lost tribes of Israel; and the Scandinavian literature tells us how they came with horses across the steppes from "the roof of the world" (probably the Caucasus), to somewhere near Riga, where some broke off towards Germany, whilst the remainder crossed the Upsala in Sweden, and there lived long as priests of Father Odin.

They were said to be distinguished by a mark on the forehead, which was probably artificial, but may well be the two perpendicular wrinkles which are seldom seen except upon the brows of their descendants. As a non-warlike clan they increased mightily in numbers, and when the migration of Swedes from the East became inconveniently pressing, they moved to Wermaland near the great lakes Wener and Wetter.

Here the pressure of the Swedes, in course of time, cramped them again; and as they were particularly well-informed about the fertile islands of the West, the whole race crossed the sea to our eastern coasts, and from East Anglia and Northumbria spread rapidly all over the country.

Christianity has long submerged their religion, but the children still worship the old god with the long white beard; he comes each year at Yuletide from Norway in a sledge drawn over the ice by reindeer, and in the old kindly Pagan way he brings presents for everybody. They have re-christened him Santa Claus; but he still comes down the chimney, for in the old days the chimneys were large enough for such a visit, being no more than a great hole in the centre of the roof, always open to the heavens.

The religion of Odin was not only based upon good cheer and the procession of the seasons --- it elevated the telling of the truth into the greatest of the virtues, and despised the quibbles and craftiness of the southern peoples, which plain folk still call lies. Also, it inculcated a belief in fair play and sportsmanship towards an enemy, which raised the exploits of the warlike Danes, Norsemen and Saxons on to a higher and cleaner level than those of the lesser peoples, among whom cruelty and cowardice held sway.

The essentially pacific character of the Angles themselves has been lost sight of in view of the most picturesque feature of their religion, which was the provision of a special Heaven or Valhalla

33

for the heroes who died fighting. These favoured spirits spent every day hunting or fighting, and in the evening they were conveyed by Valkyries --- splendid women --- to gorgeous feasts of pork and ale, with singing and good fellowship. There was no fear of the thunder and lightning which now terrify degenerate souls, for it was well known to be nothing but the sound of the fighting up above, and the hurling of great bolts more in jest than anger.

The common people, however, had no part in this attractive paradise; and as they never fought for fighting's sake, but offered reason and compromise, they were welcomed by the petty rulers of the land, and gradually became the most important of its inhabitants.

These Angles had no particular quarrel with the Normans, and made no opposition to the advance of William le Meschin's army, which gradually worked round by Workington and Whitehaven to Ravenglass itself, and thus almost cut Earl Boethar and his people off from the sea.

The city of Barnscar was lost and eventually razed to the ground; a commencement was made with Muncaster Castle which gradually grew from a circuit of wooden stockades into a strong Norman fortification, and William assembled most of his army there and drove Earl Boethar's people into the hills.

The offensive, however, was not pressed because William Meschin himself was short of men. Trouble had come upon the Normans from a new direction. Dolfin, the son of the old Earl Gospatric, had kept himself fully informed of the gradual weakening of Ranulf Earl of Carlisle and had at last organised a strong Scottish backing and seized his ancestral city.

William Meschin lent men to his brother for the recapture of Carlisle, and Ranulf himself did his utmost to retrieve the position, but it was hopeless. The whole country was rising, and William's little army was cut off from that of his brother.

The loss of Ravenglass had been a serious matter for Earl Boethar, but not a fatal one. He had always received more or less food through the depôt which Olaf Tryggvesson had established near the foot of Crummock Water, and now he had to depend on it almost entirely. Traces of it exist at the present day, and it is shown on the Ordnance Survey Map as a Peel, but originally it was an oblong Scandinavian fortification built upon a low hill or island among the marshes which lay between Loweswater and Crummock. The paths to it were devious and difficult to the uninitiated, but they were safe for pack horses, and communicated with Workington and many landing places on the Derwent, as well as with all the Scandinavian villages towards the sea, such as Rowrah, Lamplugh and Mockerkin.

If the Normans ever captured it, as was unlikely, the garrison could easily escape along Crummock Water by the boats which were kept for ferrying grain to the Earl's water-mill, so it was a particularly safe place. The site of this mill can also be still traced in a beautiful glen which lies in front of the windows of the modern Victoria Hotel, at Buttermere, where on the right side of the mill-stream the rock has been carved out in the shape of a crescent to accommodate a water-wheel, which apparently was balanced by a similar wheel on the other side, so that the stream was forced between them and caused them to turn. From each of these wheels a shaft rose vertically, passing through the floor of the milling chamber which was built over the stream. In this chamber were two pairs of millstones, one pair directly operated by each shaft, without any machinery or gearing. This mill had been constructed about a hundred years before by Boethar's ancestress, the great Shelagh, who brought two men named Blake from Ireland to build it for her on the model of those in Norway, and in particular, of one the Norsemen had built near Galway, which is working to this day.

Storehouses and a bakery were apparently erected on the site now occupied by the hotel, and it is probable that the food was sent out in the form of

BUTTERIKELD (M> Pearson)

flat rye cakes with which Viking ships used to be provisioned. These have the merit of never becoming dry; and having eaten them with butter in Norway I know them to be good. Here also an armourer's shop was erected for the repair of battle-axes, spears, etc., and body armour, and for the forging of the barbs of arrows. The place was afterwards used as a blacksmith's shop for hundreds of years.

The armour captured from the Normans found a ready sale in Scotland and Ireland; little of it was used by the defenders as they preferred leathern jerkins covered with small metal rings which were sewn on most thickly where they were likely to be most wanted. These would turn any ordinary blow without being too heavy.

Many a poor soul died under torture rather than reveal the position of this secret valley, and the need for keeping silence about the routes and passes was so ingrained that until the Middle Ages paths like the Styhead were kept secret.

It has recently been found that Earl Boethar took the precaution of fortifying the dry triangle of land near the foot of the Scale Beck, where it enters Crummock Water, instead of trusting entirely to the protection of the marshes in the direction of Floutern Tarn and Ennerdale. The stone from these defences was long ago taken away for building walls, and the earth which remained is covered in Summer with the bracken which obscures everything. It was, however, obvious that Earl Boethar was sure to complete his defences by making this unlikely route secure; and upon making a proper search in the Spring before the bracken grew, I found clear traces of intelligible fortifications which are neither Roman nor ancient British, just about where one would expect them to be.

CHAPTER VI

WILLIAM RUFUS

For five years after the death of William I the lull continued; the Normans were busy among themselves ousting the eldest son out of his inheritance; but at last King William Rufus felt that it was necessary to prove himself a successful general and a great King, and rid the North of that arch-rebel Boethar and the impudent Dolfin who had actually captured Carlisle.

Rufus liked Ranulf Meschin himself, and did not blame him much for the loss of the armies which had been entrusted to him. They had obviously been insufficient for their purpose, and now existed only as scattered garrisons at Kendal and in the upper Eden Valley. Ranulf had the necessary knowledge and experience for a thorough conquest of Cumberland and Westmorland, and the King decided to back him up with an overpowering army, and go North himself for the glory of the victory.

King William II was a headstrong man who abandoned many an enterprise before it was complete; but he made his commencements gloriously and extravagantly, and certainly he brought adequate forces to Kendal for the subjection of

Lakeland, and announced in advance that the task was done.

Thus, in 1092 he pushed on in full force from Kendal Castle to Staveley Town, and marched to Ambleside, which he considered the capital of Lakeland. He gave orders for the permanent strengthening of the Roman *castrum,* and hoped to capture the roads to the right and left towards Penrith and Ravenglass, both of which points were already held by the soldiers of Ranulf and William Meschin. Further there was the broad track to be clearly seen, which Edmund Ironside had followed towards his victory further North, and which was still in use.

No wonder the Red King considered the work to be already done, and his friends in England rejoiced accordingly. His descent on Ambleside was a Royal Progress; the whole of the lakeside was occupied, and as there were no weak communications to be cut, Earl Boethar's people could only watch from the mountains with the dreadful feeling that war on this scale was too much for them, and that there was nothing more to be done but make peace.

With all the panoply of glorious war King William II occupied what remained of the Roman city of Galena or Ambleside; tents and pavilions were set up on the pleasant flat lands at the head of Windermere lake, armoured knights and gay banners passed to and fro, fine ladies graced the scene, tournaments celebrated the victory, and the King himself, young and sanguine, centre and head of Norman chivalry, distributed his favours. He was the fountain of honour, the bestower of patronage, who could ennoble any man or woman with a word, --- and he felt himself a god.

Meanwhile Earl Boethar, with his brother and his friends, felt their helplessness. It was time to make peace and not war. All England had been conquered; even the brave Hereward, son of Godiva and Leofric, had given in; Scotland would give no help; all the coast from Ravenglass to Maryport was more or less occupied by the Normans; Dolfin would be crushed at Carlisle; and there was no help to be expected from any direction. Clearly it was time to stop and make any terms that could be got.

Without loss of time a Thingmote was held in Little Langdale, and it was decided to send an embassy with flags of truce, and offer to hold all Lakeland in future for the King under whatever lords he might appoint; also to offer to guarantee the safety of the King's soldiers and convoys going to or from Carlisle or Scotland; and finally to offer that their present rulers would sail beyond the sea, or serve King William, as he might prefer.

Young Ackin offered to be the ambassador, but the meeting was against him, and chose the vener-

41

able Ari Knudson to be its spokesman, with four other white-bearded men to support him. If the King would accept Earl Boethar, he would be his man on any decent terms; but if the new King was harsh he would take his family to Scotland, and the people would be glad to serve under Ranulf or anybody else.

There was no advantage in delay, and next morning the little embassy set out with white flags of truce and green branches. They took no arms nor anything likely to give offence, and the Thingmote waited in Little Langdale for their return.

CHAPTER VII

THE ORIGINAL "OLD HARRY"

When the embassy encountered the Norman outposts it was treated respectfully, and a guard was sent in with it towards Ambleside, where it was turned over to a superior officer, who questioned the old men and found out all about their offer.

The embassy did not see an enclosure full of half naked girls close at hand, with their wrists bound behind them --- the raw material for some lascivious orgy --- but their existence probably influenced the subsequent interview. King William II is described in the *Victoria History* as being unspeakably immoral, violent, boastful, and profane, and probably his camp contained other evidences as well as these poor naked girls.

(When William II was killed in 1100, men looked upon his death as a judgment from God. He was buried at Winchester without any religious service, a stern and surprising proof of the backbone of the bishops in those days).

When the old men were taken in to the King's Council, Ari Knudson looked a commanding figure, with his long white beard. He was six feet high and singularly straight and ruddy for a man beyond three score years and ten. His four companions

looked gaunt and weather-worn, but they stood together with dignity while a Norman lord said he
had questioned them in their own language, and
they said they had come from a Thingmote of the
rebels in the mountains to treat for peace.

The King sat scowling at them, but suddenly he
rose and shouted:

"The men are spies, put out their eyes". Nobody
moved. "Put out their eyes", he said. "Eustace,
there, you see to it".

The officer to whom the order was given took a
dozen soldiers, who surrounded the embassy and
gouged out the eyes of the five men amidst shrieks
of agony.

When the soldiers stood aside old Ari alone
stood upon his feet, for his companions were writh-
ing in agony upon the floor. His arms were still
bound behind him, his blood was on his face and
beard, but he thought of nothing but his duty.

"Let me speak, let me speak", he cried in the
King's language. "We are ambassadors come to
offer peace" --- and this he repeated many times.

But the King said: "Take them away, they have
had their answer". And that was the end of it.

They were dragged away to the kennels, which
served for a prison, and there lay in agony whilst
the King himself enjoyed the excitement of having
done an evil deed. It lent a frenzy to the feast that

44

night, and helped his Majesty to "feel like a god".

. . . . . .

At last, with all its brilliant pagentry, the Royal army moved out from Ambleside, and advanced along the Rothay towards Dunmail Raise. Very slowly it passed Rydal Water and approached Grasmere in great force, fighting the outposts. Earl Boethar had a large army, but it lay partly in the Elterwater direction, and nothing more than delaying actions could be fought at Rydal, though it is worthy of note that this favourable ground was held tenaciously afterwards.

Gradually the head of the Norman army passed round the eastern side of Grassmere, and it could be seen that in the centre they carried a group of five standards with one higher than the rest. Few English could make it out, but the Norman soldiery knew what it was, and in some sub-conscious way their knowledge affected their superstitious souls afterwards.

It was the naked body of a tall old man with a long white beard. He was crucified upon a framework like a door, and his legs were stretched apart to show that he had been shamefully mutilated and disembowelled. Poor old Ari --- who could tell what efforts had been made to break his noble spirit before death released him?

The Normans were in close formation making a triumphal progress, when they heard a roaring sound behind them. It was louder than anything they had heard before, and I, who have heard it on a smaller scale, would describe it as like an express train rushing through a small, close railway station. The water of the lake rose up to the sky in clouds of spray, and their regiments and horsemen were struck great blows and hurled to the ground by something invisible. Every tree was lifted from its roots and flung down among the soldiers, whilst branches and all sorts of things hurtled through the air.

Camp equipment flew away, knights once down among their kicking horses never got up again, and this roaring thing, this invisible giant or demon, flew like the wind among them, throwing men over, striking some dead and wounding others, until the whole army fell into panic.

(The phenomenon of the "Helm wind", which sometimes lasts for three days, is caused by a collision of two weather systems among the mountains. It generally originates in the long valley running North and South near Crossfell, and it is said that the clouds coming up from the East do not mingle with those coming from the West, but form long

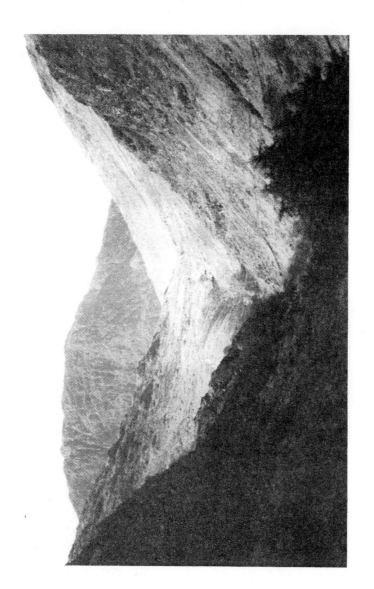

WILD FIGHTING COUNTRY ON THE STYHEAD (M. Pearson).

lines with a lane of clear sky between them; and the wind beneath forms an acute disturbance over a curiously localised area, which is sometimes in one valley, sometimes in another).

The accursed standards were thrown down, for every man thought the wrath of God had overtaken them in consequence of the King's inhuman cruelty. They saw that in the East the sky was a livid yellow, and was it not to the East that the monks turned when they said the "Credo", the mysterious East where Christ was done to death like these five men? It was the wrath of God which was upon them --- and, cutting down those who tried to stem the panic, King William's soldiers threw away both arms and armour and ran back towards Ambleside!

The King himself was very much afraid, and the tradition says that he ran all the way to Kendal; but this, of course, is a humorous exaggeration designed to finish up the story in a vivid way.

The truth was that he got back to Ambleside in safety, though Boethar's men killed thousands of his unarmed soldiers as they followed him. The tremendous wind blew for three days, and when the English realised that God had sent the "Helm wind" to help them they went freely among the scattered and demoralised Normans and never ceased from slaying.

The "Helm wind" is an extraordinary phenomenon, curiously local in its area, and all Lakeland dwellers are familiar with stories about it; but to the Norman French it must have been an awful experience; and those that got back to Ambleside were so impressed and shaken by what they regarded as God's judgment upon the King's wickedness that they could hardly be persuaded to mount the defences, and if an attack had been made at that time they would hardly have resisted.

It is evident from the howes or burial places of this period about Grassmere that Earl Boethar had plenty of time to bury his dead, but nobody knows whether he buried any of the invaders, or merely stripped their bodies and left them, as a deterrent and object lesson to the Normans if they renewed the advance.

(The burial places prior to the Norwegian period are shown as "barrows", and are embodied in place names as 'ber' and 'bar', such as Howber Hill, Langbar).

The greatest and most honoured burial place was, however, on top of the hill, to which he conveyed the body of his dead envoy or messenger, his "lyp" in the old Norse language. His howe and that of his companions at Grassmere (Butterlyp Howe) will proclaim Ari Knudson's story until its name changes, and that, I think, will never happen; and though we speak of "Old Harry" without knowing who he was (except that it was somebody entirely English and not Continental) there is a tradition in the Harrison family which fits the facts.

To King William II, and his lieutenant Ranulf Meschin, the lovely scenery of Rydal and Grassmere must have spoiled their taste for sylvan beauty ever afterwards; for the one would always associate it with God's anger against his brutality, and the other with the downfall of his hopes of finishing this long war, which had disgraced him as being the only Norman noble who had not been able to take the land which had been given to him.

With all his efforts and glorious hopes, he was no further forward than when he had previously captured Ambleside, and found himself unable to hold it. He garrisoned the place, and then marched with the King to Kendal, and so on to Carlisle, with reinforcements, and priests to make a show of religion, to reassure the shaken army, and make it feel that God was now with it.

Dolfin had no help from the Scottish King, and all his support was unofficial, but he defended Carlisle so tenaciously that it was badly knocked to pieces when at last he was forced to relinquish it and flee to Scotland. King William rebuilt its defences and appointed a great priest to administer it jointly with Ranulf Meschin, who was now really

Earl of Carlisle again, with a large army and a free hand for the capture of Lakeland. But King William went South again without revisiting Ambleside or making any further effort to put down what he considered to be an impudent rebellion.

HONISTER PASS (looking down towards Buttermere -C. Negus)

CHAPTER VIII

THE ROMAN ROADS

Another chapter now commenced in the long struggle for Lakeland. Ranulf had more men than ever, and proceeded to carry out his orders to capture the Roman roads from Ambleside to Ravenglass and Penrith. The route from Kendal to Carlisle was well garrisoned, and the country from Carlisle to "Spatrie", Gospatric's old place of residence was again in Norman hands.

The route from Ambleside to Grassmere was left alone, possibly because the bones of the unburied dead would injure the morale of the army, and instead the Norman army moved up Little Langdale and held it in force. Then, without delay, they pushed out along the road and held Wrynose pass and Wrynose Bottom, places as bleak as any to be found in England, and sacred to the memory of King Ethelred's surrender to Earl Grice long ago. Finally, at a good deal of expense, they captured the Hardknott Pass and Castle, and forced their way down Eskdale to join hands with William Meschin at Muncaster Castle.

Ranulf could now show his master that real progress had been made, but the enterprise did not turn

51

out well. The country was unsuited to the Frenchmen and their horses, and the line could not be held; the evening mists were full of hard fighting men, who broke through in a different place each night. They could run up and down the mountains as easily as the men who now compete in fell races, and woe to any Normans who tried to follow them.

Outclassed in archery, and harried every night, the Norman forces slowly melted away; they were occupying one of the wet sections of the Lake District, and when Ranulf himself returned from Carlisle he gave up the idea of holding the road. Thereafter he confined himself to raids, but even these sometimes turned out badly, because, while the safe ones towards Hawkshead and Coniston had little influence on the campaign, those in the direction of the secret valley often led to the raiders getting bogged or lost among the uncharted mountains.

(The wettest area in the Lake District is contained within a triangle drawn from the Langdale Pikes to Scafell and Gt. Gable. When the wind blows from this area it carries a certain amount of extra rain with it; hence a South wind [or South-West] is bad for Buttermere and Keswick, a West wind for Grassmere, and a North wind for Coniston. Windermere suffers if the wind blows from the North-West; but in common with the rest of the country, it also gets rain with a South-West wind, and thus all that part of Westmorland seems to have more than its proper share. Motorists passing along Windermere in the rain, with a North or West wind, find they can soon run into fine weather by keeping on beyond Dunmail Raise. They are merely acting like the sea-captains who circumnavigate a disturbed area, and run round bad weather. Like Scotland, the Lake District generally gets very fine weather in April, May and June, and droughts are not infrequent).

In carrying out his orders about the northern road from Ambleside to Penrith, Ranulf was still more unfortunate. The Normans marched up the Troutbeck in all their bravery from some point near the present Low Wood Hotel, and captured Earl Ackin's depôt and camp at Froswick, where he had been waiting a month for them. Falling back rapidly, he had trailed them along High Street, that cloud-covered ridge, past the straits of Riggindale and Kidsty Pike, until in the most desperate country large reinforcements joined him and he fell upon his enemy in the night. The men he lost were buried on Raven Howe, and this, of course, marks the place of battle, but it does not mark how the fleeing foe, high up above the world on those misty heights, was pursued and harried in the darkness, so that very few got back to Froswick and Ambleside. Even this remnant of a force had better have been lost, because the men sapped the courage of everyone they spoke to, and all the old tales of wizards and enchantments were revived, so that the Ambleside army became ineffective and little or nothing could be done with it.

.   .   .   .

About this time Ranulf le Meschin obtained some real help from a spy. Hitherto the feeling of loyalty towards Earl Boethar and the refugees had been so great that men and women would die upon the rack rather than say a word which might help the enemy; and no real spy could possibly penetrate into the secret valley which controlled the rebel activities, and supplied both food and arms (as well as reinforcements) wherever they were needed.

But now a new feeling began to make itself felt in England. People realised that the Normans had come to stay, and felt that it was no longer any use to fight against them. Indeed, there were some who longed so sincerely for peace that they were impatient of the long-drawn-out struggle of their fellow-countrymen, and would have sacrificed their own brothers rather than give the Normans an excuse for a continuance of the cruel and bad methods of government which they said the rebellion justified.

Among these people was a man Jackson the herder, who had been in the secret valley with cattle, and to whom the hope of reward appealed so strongly that he sent word to the Norman lord that he would tell him all he knew. He called the place "Little Norway" and told Ranulf that there was no way to it from Ambleside except for birds. The route he knew was along the broad valley from Penrith to Keswick, and then he advised his hearer to cross between the two lakes, and bear round to the left by Stair, along the valley which is now called Newlands.

To the best of his ability, this man told his noble patron how he had driven cattle on and on, until they came to a great double elbow in the path at Keskadale; a place which he said was sure to be defended, but which he thought an army might avoid by keeping to the left.

Further on, however, he described the steep pass near the waterfall, so steep that one could hardly climb at all, and said that nothing could save the army from the necessity of storming it. Here he said an awful battle would have to be fought; but as the secret valley was surrounded on all sides by similar ridges, or worse ones, this route was Ranulf's one chance of success.

"And now tell me what 'Little Norway' is like", said Ranulf, full of curiosity and the desire to visualise the work when it was done.

"It is a fearsome place, my lord, full of enchantments; an evil place where the red fire of hell makes the fields fertile, coming as it does of a Summer's evening for no more than a few minutes, and leaving the rye tall and nearly ready for harvest next morning". (In 1930 it commenced on May 21st.)

Jackson said that the fields facing South yielded one crop after another owing to this extraordinary arrangement, and that they fed thousands of men and women, for the valley was full of people. There were two lakes, he said, covered with geese and ducks, and full of fish, which came up simply to be caught; so there was never any lack of food. Also there were great herds of swine across the lake, which fed among the trees, and no shortage of sheep or cattle, because they bred like magic.

The herder seemed to be intoxicated with his own description, but Ranulf pressed him upon exactly what he had seen in proper sequence after crossing the top of the pass.

"First, lord, I saw the great crater of a burning mountain, all black upon one side and red upon the other --- a dull glowing red --- and from it magic water boiled over and fell, all hot and sizzling; and round about there seemed to be half a dozen great black mountains like the stumps of a witch's teeth; and all about were fearsome descents into the enchanted lakes.

"Yes, lord, they are surely as I say, for everything about is double. I saw my own cattle before I was paid for them --- two herds instead of one , the very self-same beasts, all walking upside down. And the woods go under the lake as well --- under both lakes, I mean, my lord --- and they said the one crop was as good as the other, the one in the lake I mean, and the corn grows again every time the red light touches it. It is a fearsome place".

"But I have heard many times", said Ranulf, "that it is the most beautiful place under Heaven".

"Yes, but 'tis the beauty of enchantment. God preserve me from such beauty as that", and Jackson went on to tell of the wooden huts in which the people lived, the great manor house, where he had been paid, the water-mill with a bakery opposite, the perpetual clanging at the anvil, the boats upon the lake bringing men and food, and all the ordered busy-ness of a well arranged community.

Once again Ranulf went over the description of the route up Newlands valley with Jackson, for already he visualised himself at the head of a great army sweeping all before it, and finally extinguishing for ever the foulest centre of enchantment and iniquity of which he had ever heard.

(The red light, "like a ray from the furnaces of hell", is seen occasionally about sunset in May, June, and July. It originates in the setting sun and is similar to that seen in the Dolomites. The water overflowing from the tarn near the Red Pike, is not really hot, but it seems so, and as the stone beneath it is partly green and partly red it is called the Sour Milk Ghyll. The extraordinary reflections for which Buttermere and Crummock Water are famous, account for Jackson's preposterous tale about the crops and herds being doubled, the reflection often seeming to be more real than the reality).

· · · · · · ·

Meantime William Rufus was killed in the New Forest, and little enquiry was made into the how or why. His unspeakable immoralities led the ecclesiastical authorities at Winchester to refuse him a Christian burial, though they allowed him to be put into the Cathedral.

After this there was further delay as King Henry was well disposed towards the Scottish, and took time to decide whether it would not be best to withdraw and save his face by turning the Lakeland Earl and his wild country over to the Scottish King. Finally, however, he confirmed the previous policy, and backed up Le Meschin with more men for a new enterprise with Penrith and Lowther Castles for its base.

Ranulf now attacked the broad valley which runs by Threlkeld to Keswick. An overwhelming army of horse and foot marched over the great commons to the River Greta, and established themselves south of Keswick on a hill which they fortified with wooden stockades and excellent earthworks. The harrying of the advance of this army was difficult, as the high fells were further apart, and though the long line of communications was often cut, the Normans managed to increase their hold on Borrowdale and Bassenthwaite in a manner which was dangerous to the secret valley, which, with Jackson the Herder's help, they had nearly located.

Earl Boethar no longer had an unlimited army, but owing to this menace he concentrated his men at Buttermere or thereabouts and made the Norman raids into Borrowdale and Newlands Vale very expensive.

At last Ranulf Meschin made a very definite move by marching the bulk of his army round by Portinscale to Stair, where a camp was made preparatory to a great advance which was like the beginning of the end. Keeping their left wing upon Derwentwater, the Normans fought their way by Gill Bank to Little Town, knowing that Earl Boethar's headquarters lay somewhere in front of them, but how near or how far away time was to show. Here they were confronted by four valleys like the fingers of a hand; all were well defended, and none knew which to take. Time was wanted for reconnoitring and clearing them out, and a camping place was chosen where Newlands church now stands. It was a better site in those days than now, because the land has since been drained, but as the place was surrounded on three sides by water courses, and as the streams ran through a very boggy place and were guarded by vigilant sentries, the weary army eventually took its rest, the men lying as it were with "their arms in their hands".

Little did Armand de Fécamp, the deputy commander, think that, when his enemies had fallen back that day from the Catbells, their retreat had been controlled from a mountain on his right, now called Ackin's Howe, and that a very large force of men had been kept deliberately out of his sight, so that he might spend the night in a convenient position for his enemies, whose headquarters were only three miles away.

In the middle of the night amidst a downpour of rain, the whole countryside seemed to come to life. Thousands of well-armed men without lights gathered on every side, passed through the morasses, and turned the camp into a shambles. There was no escape, and the first little church at Newlands was afterwards erected to mark the place of that grim butchery.

Ranulf himself was still at Keswick, ready to bring his rear-guard along next day and lead his

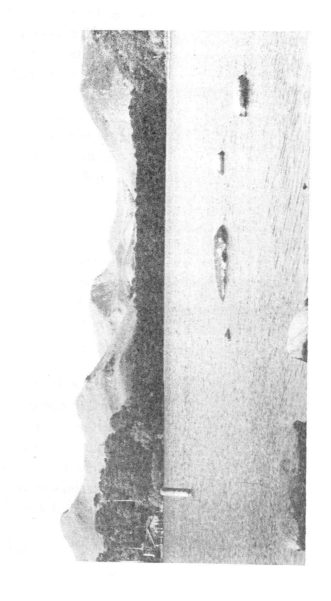

DERWENTWATER WITH CATBELLS (Penny Moreton/Allerdale Borough Council)

army to the final assault upon the secret valley. Bitterly he upbraided Armand de Fécamp, but Armand was dead, his tawny hair and fierce blue eyes pressed deep into the mud by the struggling crowd which had fought near to where his tent had stood.

Of the fugitives who had escaped none could tell much about what had happened, for it was as though a million men or demons had swept over them in the darkness and then disappeared. Ranulf could not go to see the place, as his supports had already been driven back to Stair, and his enemies were following up their victory by pressing down Borrowdale as well as Newlands, and getting behind to cut him off from Penrith.

It was no use letting them besiege him at Keswick as they evidently expected to do, and he appears to have made a masterly withdrawal by the Roman road or Terrace walk along the east side of Bassenthwaite Lake to "Spatrie" (which is now spelt Aspatria), where the remains of his army joined that of his brother William in territory which had already been conquered and fortified.

And thus ended another chapter in the relentless war against our persecuted ancestors, who had enjoyed no peace since Edward the Confessor's death, --- a Saint who sold or gave his country to the foreigner, and his countrymen to wholesale butchery, which reduced our population to about 2 millions.

61

CHAPTER IX

A LULL

By bitter experience the Normans had learned a good deal about Lakeland, and now had a clear idea of the position of the secret valley which they were so anxious to attack. No Norman had ever seen it, and there were fantastic legends of its position high up among the mountain tops, or walled in by extraordinary barriers; also there were tales of its invisibility and of the enchantments which surrounded it. The extraordinary losses of the Norman armies were superstitiously put down to reasons of this kind, and as there was little real information, the most horrible stories were believed by the soldiers concerning the disappearance of their comrades apparently carried off by demons.

It is true that there were no half measures about Earl Boethar's people; they were fighting for their lives, but they were not demons. They took no prisoners, but killed the wounded and left nobody to tell where they had gone or what had happened. They pillaged the dead, and wore or sold both clothing and armour. When they were themselves captured they died with a sort of exultation, even under torture, glorying in the fact that, though the Normans could enslave the priest-ridden Saxons (worthy subjects of the miserable Edward the Confessor, who was less than a man), they could not make headway against the free men of the North. Often their bitter tongues would taunt the Normans into shortening their tortures, which indeed was good policy, for there was no escape for man, woman, or child, if they got into Norman hands. Such were both sides in Norman times, for England had gone back from civilisation to savagery.

At Aspatria (or Spatrie as it was called) the two brothers had long conferences; William was the less warlike of the two, yet he had been successful, whilst Ranulf, his splendid elder brother, had been the most unsuccessful and unfortunate commander in England. The question now to be decided was whether to relinquish all hope of conquering the mountain country, and rest content with Carlisle and the broad valley stretching towards Kendal and Lancaster (with Ambleside as a more or less detached island often cut off from its support), or whether it would be safer to try to persuade a hard and censorious King to let him try again, though one army after another had been lost.

It was very clear that the former course would cost him his Court favour, and that if he admitted in this way that he was a failure, King Henry would transfer the earldom of Carlisle to some energetic rival. For this reason the second course seemed better, and it was urged by William the more confidently because he thought he saw a good way of getting to the secret valley from his own territory near Papcastle, or even some point further west.

The King was a more intelligent man than his brother, and for a long time he refused to be persuaded to waste more troops upon Ranulf Meschin's enterprise. Thousands of men had been lost every year throughout three reigns; armies had melted away after a single battle, and nothing but Ambleside had been gained. King Henry took time to decide; in reality he wanted to weigh up Ranulf himself, the only noble who had failed to make himself master of his earldom. The verdict was favourable to Ranulf, who was of the best type of the men around him. Then the King debated with his Councillors whether it would be better to make friends with Boethar and employ Ranulf elsewhere, and when this was decided in the negative and the new Papcastle scheme was fully explained he gave his consent.

Meanwhile a couple of years had elapsed, and now Ranulf was sent to Normandy to recruit a new army, as English troops were likely to desert in Lakeland. Money was raised and an adequate force enlisted and transported to England.

There were now greater preparations than before. Papcastle was occupied in force, and as it had at one time been a Roman cavalry centre, it was soon made safe. William Meschin contributed all the men he could spare, regiments were withdrawn from Carlisle, Kendal, and all the castles of the Eden valley, and these, with the new troops recruited in Normandy, made an overwhelming army, more suited for the conquest of Scotland than of poor war-worn Earl Boethar.

CHAPTER X

GREAT PREPARATIONS

The great camp at Papcastle was protected by the River Derwent, but the audacity of the enemy across the river was extraordinary. Desperate raids were constantly being made at one point or another, and a surprising number of men were killed.

Preparations were soon made for a crossing to the triangle of land where the River Cocker runs into the Derwent, near where Cockermouth Castle now stands. The customary Springtime drought had made the passage of the Derwent an easy matter, and very soon the new camp was fortified with stockades in spite of the frenzied attacks of the English.

Once the Normans were established, however, their enemies disappeared; the open and level country about Cockermouth was very favourable to the Normans, and they gradually made themselves masters of it, suffering, however, each night from persistent attacks designed to reduce their numbers.

The Norman armament was very superior to that of the English, and their mounted men, who bestrode the ancestors of our cart horses, seemed to be irresistible. Their pikemen and spearmen were well-disciplined and partly armoured, and their morale was excellent, for they knew they were being led towards a straightforward job which exactly suited them. No more were they expected to capture mountain ridges hidden in the mist, or to traverse ravines where there was hardly any foothold. No longer would each night's camping be a nightmare. They felt at last that their leaders knew what they were about, and without doubt quiet confidence pervaded all the army.

On the English side it had long been realised that the final chapter of the struggle was very near, and to many it seemed best to give up Buttermere, as the secret valley was beginning to be called, and try to draw the Normans again into the wildest passes, where their armour and heavy horses would be a handicap instead of an advantage. No place, however, seemed so defensible as Buttermere, and as it was their depôt and arsenal, the Earl decided upon a supreme effort to defend it.

He was himself a shrewd old man whose whole life seemed to have been spent in fighting the Normans. He had a marvellous knowledge of every geographical detail of the Lake country, and seemed to be always ready to suggest some stratagem for the discomfiture of his blood-thirsty enemy. He was a kindly, humorous man, with lightish hair and a fresh complexion, long-headed in more senses than one, blue-eyed, tall and active.

He lived in a great manor house built of wood., with a square hole in the roof for smoke, and a fire in the centre of the floor. Instead of windows there were doors of which the top half opened independently of the bottom, and in each corner of the floor there were low walls three or four feet high, enclosing sleeping places filled with rugs and skins --- snug beds, well protected from the draughts.

The manor house grew, because when extensions were needed they were built upon the lean-to principle, with doors into the main house. None could say that it was inconvenient either for Summer or Winter, or for the great gatherings where there were eating and drinking, or for the conferences where speeches were made. Nothing is left of it now except the name of the Wood House, but there is a manor of the same period still to be seen in Norway, as well as lesser houses which show how people lived so long ago.

The Church or Chapel in those days was up at Gatesgarth, (the ground on which it stood is called Chapelgarth), and the valley was full of little wooden houses, for timber was plentiful in this most beautiful of all valleys. The bakery and armoury stood where three tracks met, near the watermill up the lovely glen where a good hotel now stands. There were sheep and swine on the hills, fields of oats and rye, and a deal of work and trade, so that a whole generation existed there in health and strength, helping the war in all their various ways.

Everybody knew that sooner or later the valley would be attacked from the North, but the novel defence which the Earl had been perfecting for years gave them confidence, and even when the great day came and the mothers and children were ordered to the hills they went reluctantly.

This defence which pleased them so much was nothing less than the diversion of the road or track from over the shoulder of Rannerdale Knotts, near the lake, to a narrow and dangerous valley close at hand, where everything was prepared for a great killing.

The well-worn track from the direction of Cockermouth could not go round Hause Point as it does at present, because the precipitous wall of rock sticking out into the lake had not then been blasted away. Instead, it ascended on masses of fallen earth and stone further to the eastward. Laboriously the Earl had all this mass of rubbish removed for one hundred and twenty yards, so that there was no longer any way on to the Knotts, nor any suggestion that a path had ever been there.

(Eight hundred years of falling stones and soil, together with the subsequent efforts to restore the old path, so necessary to the village, led to the present makeshift track which, however, has never been as good as the remainder of the broken road).

He provided a boat for his own people to go round the point, but he created a beautiful new path further to the left, winding up Rannerdale valley, and still traceable near the top.

This new path was almost as wide as a road in places, but it led nowhere. It crossed and recrossed the stream on faulty bridges, and where it vanished into the trees he concealed pits filled with stakes, and every contrivance and snare for killing men and horses.

In its wild beauty there is no prettier spot in England than Rannerdale in bluebell time; and after Earl Boethar constructed his trap, the lush vegetation had a year or two for covering up the work of man and obliterating the original pathway. Right at the top of the dale, near the surprise view, the new path was clearly to be seen from below encouraging the stranger to go forward, and also providing a good route for Boethar's own people from the surprise view down towards the prepared battlefield.

(The "surprise view" is twenty minutes walk from the Victoria Hotel at Buttermere; it gives a glimpse of Crummock Water, Loweswater, the Solway, and Galloway beyond.)

The removal of the old path was a very sound piece of strategy, because if the attackers knew the old route, it presented them with an unclimbable wall of rock to get round or over, an obstacle which they might besiege with ladders for weeks before it could be passed. Whereas if they did not know the exact route they would be sure to get into difficulties in Rannerdale valley, which even today shows signs of having been cut up in a bewildering fashion.

The unexpected multitude of the army at Cockermouth, however, seems to have alarmed Earl Boethar, as the defences at Brackenthwaite were largely increased at the last moment, so that the invaders might, perhaps, be defeated upon the road near the narrow place where the slopes of Whiteside come down towards the lake.

CHAPTER XI

THE BATTLE AT BRACKENTHWAITE

Upon a cloudless Summer day the great Norman army began to move at Cockermouth. There was a sparkling quality in the air, a Scottish briskness from across the Solway, which seemed to bless and caress the enterprise. In the forefront there was a holy Bishop, surrounded by monks and acolytes, to bid the army God-speed. Censers were swung, and the incense rose into a cloud, as the religious group stood still to see the army pass. Chants were sung and prayers were said to consecrate the enterprise, for were these not the loyal soldiers of King Henry, marching irresistibly to clear out the last remaining rebel stronghold in this conquered land of England?

See the great body of armoured knights, with their standards and pennons, their great horses, and their squires in attendance --- are they not irresistible? See the splendid regiments of foot, the backbone of the army, rank upon rank in their thousands, and behind all, the endless lines of packhorses with baggage, food and tents. Such an army of men has never been seen since at Cockermouth.

Ranulf Meschin, Earl of Carlisle, bade farewell to his noble brother William. One had to stay behind to maintain supplies, and besides, the honour of capturing the secret valley, cause of all the trouble which had threatened Ranulf with ruin, was not a thing to be shared with anybody.

"Adieu, my brother", cried William, "and I only hope they will stand and fight, instead of trailing you into those evil mountains once again, for they are as elusive as hobgoblins. Adieu". He turned away ill-pleased, thinking that Ranulf played the elder brother too much, and that it would have been more in keeping with the facts to have made this last act of the drama into a joint enterprise.

The Normans marched with the swamps of the River Cocker upon their right; these marshes no longer exist, as the river accepted narrower limits when it was cleared out, but they were very real in the old days, and to a great extent they protected the Royal army. Earl Boethar's people kept in touch with the advance without much loss to themselves, as their archers, with their clumsy bows, had been provided with the ponies which had formerly been employed as pack-horses, and these enabled them to keep out of range of the feebler Norman archery, while themselves taking a heavy toll in dead and wounded men.

The heavy longbow had become a weapon of precision in the hands of these experts, so that even an armoured knight was not safe, because his horse might be brought down, as well as his half-armoured squire. The Norman archers were out-classed both in accuracy and range; they were not trained to aim each individual arrow, but excelled in the rapidity with which they could maintain a flight of arrows at close quarters, and later on they got their opportunity.

At Lorton the Normans halted for two nights and a day, which was spent in exploring the Whinlatter Pass and entrenching bodies of archers at strategic points, so that on the second morning Ranulf felt it safe to move forward again, and in the afternoon joined issue with his enemy at Brackenthwaite, where the steep slopes of Whiteside approach the Cocker, and narrow Lorton Vale into a defensible position.

Here all sorts of earthworks had been made and superhuman efforts were put forth to stop the Normans; but their heavy cavalry was irresistible, and the rapid fire of their archers more than counterbalanced the steadiness of their opponents. The magnitude of the battle is shown by the need for six burial places in the immediate neighbourhood (Cornhow, Picket Howe, Palace Howe, Turner Howe, Backhows, and Brackenthwaite Howe); but it is evident that the Norman victory was an expensive one, and that the English got more or less safely away into Lanthwaite Woods on the one side and up the Coledale Pass on the other.

The Normans camped upon the field of battle, while the English on the West would be ferried along the lake, and those in the Coledale Pass would march home in a couple of hours by crossing the neck of Grassmoor and the easy ridge down Whiteless Pike.

The Normans had the vigour and spirit which comes of victory, but they were no longer the overwhelming body of men that had set out from Cockermouth. With the dawn of the day they searched the Lanthwaite Woods and Coledale Pass for enemies, and finding by midday that there was no danger on either side, Ranulf pushed on with his diminished army.

He had the broad lake of Crummock Water on his right and the unclimbable slopes of Grassmoor up on his left, so that, without knowing exactly how far or near his objective might be, he recognised that it would be better to make his final advance now whilst his troops were flushed with victory, than run the risks of battles each night upon his lines of communication if he delayed.

CRUMMOCK WATER FROM RANNERDALE (M. Pearson),

CHAPTER XII

THE BATTLE OF RANNERDALE

Rannerdale Knotts are like a series of knuckles crowning a long ridge with precipitous sides. The hill provides a splendid view, though not much more than a thousand feet high; and it seems to hang over Crummock Water while the country is spread like a map from the Solway to Great Gable, which is the centre of everything in Lakeland.

Here sat Earl Boethar with his son Gille, and his trusty brother Ackin watching the approach of the Norman army. The night had been spent in reorganisation instead of sleep, and now all was ready for the supreme struggle.

The mounted archers were falling back before the Normans as before, and they were keeping away from the lake, as they well knew that their task was to draw the enemy up Rannerdale to the prepared positions. Many a good shot they got in with their clumsy looking bows, which the Normans had once derided, but long afterwards adopted; and they were well content when the advance guard drove them to the lower slopes of Whiteless Pike, with Rannerdale at their feet, and the false road showing the enemy the way to nowhere.

The pick of the English army, however, lay out of sight near Crummock Water, and they could have held the point against the whole Norman host if it had tried to get round or over it by the old route. Such a thing was, however, only likely to happen if some traitor had betrayed the preparations, and none of the poor souls that the Normans captured would be likely to say a word even under torture.

As the army approached, a strong Norman scouting party came along the lakeside, and examined this point where the precipitous rock ran out into the lake. They found that there was no shallow water, and no danger from that quarter, except for as many enemies as might come round in boats. Leaving a score of men as a guard, they worked along the rock itself towards the left, and apparently decided that it was unclimbable. True they were hampered all the time by the archers who were apparently the only guard, but as there was nothing but bare rock to see, it is not surprising that they had no suspicion. In any case no army could have been taken up the face of the hill.

Slowly the critical moment arrived and passed; the Normans spread more and more to their own left, and kept along the Rannerdale Beck with their centre on the new path. Here and there they could see it a mile ahead, leading straight as they thought to that stronghold which for thirty years had given them so much trouble and loss --- a thousand curses upon it.

Perhaps it lay just at the top of that narrow route, perhaps a few miles further on, but in any case it would soon be captured. Ranulf Meschin had seen victories before as well as defeats, and he now felt that the opposition had gone to pieces. There were elaborate earthworks at the entrance to Rannerdale valley, but they were not resolutely held, and the soldiers of the enemy seemed more concerned to save their skins than had been the case on the previous day.

Doubtless he looked upon this as one of the effects of the defeat, and of his rapid advance with such a great army. "So much the worse for them", he thought, "if they throw away the chance of defending this narrow valley"; for he had long ago decided to act with the greatest ruthlessness. Man, woman and child, he thought, should be killed, in order to make an end for ever of the difficulty which had nearly ruined his life. Everything in the valley should be burnt, and left ruined for all time, as a monument and a warning of the folly of those who rebelled against the King's Majesty.

He would occupy every corner of his great earldom with a vengeance, and make it pay for all the trouble it had given him; *"vae victis"* --- what could they expect? At any rate he rode forward as an executioner; he would make an end of them forever --- oh, happy day!

CHAPTER XIII

VICTORY

By this time the noble Ranulf and the main part of his army were well within the valley of Rannerdale, and it was evident that the enemy were going to make a stand a little higher up. There were walls and ditches beyond the trees, and they were being held with determination by battle-axe and spearmen, covered by archers on the higher ground. The Earl of Carlisle pressed forward, as indeed did all ranks, and a massed attack was ordered, so as to get through the valley as quickly as possible.

Suddenly an outcry was heard in the rear. Earl Ackin, with thousands of well-armed men, the pick of his brother's army, had descended the rocks down dangerous paths, or had been put round in boats and rafts, so that a swarm of them had charged through the camp followers, and, being joined by men waiting on the opposite side of the valley, had occupied an earthwork which had been made for the purpose, and they were already pressing forward so as to cramp and crush the Normans into one another's way, and these, being taken by surprise, were not unanimous about what was to be done first.

Simultaneously the English on all sides threw

themselves into the attack and disclosed their great numbers, swollen in the rear ranks by women. Thus Ranulf found himself in a narrow place, surrounded by an unexpected multitude of enemies. It was like a bad dream; all was chaos and terror, for none knew whether to push forward or rush backward towards more open ground. Thus they became massed together and got into each other's way as Boethar and Ackin had expected.

Loud signals were given with horns, and at different points well-armed and armoured men fell into a Norse formation like a spear-head, and pushed forward among the Normans, left-handed men to the left, right-handed to the right, champion axe-wielders at the apex, pushing forward into the crowd, knee deep in dead and dying.

Ranulf decided to get out of this accursed valley, as it was no use trying to push on. His trumpeters sounded the retirement, and thus his formations were reversed and everything was blocked.

The spear-heads cut into them in all directions, the archers on the ridge were reinforced by women and poured arrows into the mass, while from the slopes of Whiteless Pike and Grassmoor there was a wild pressure of fearless men exulting in the great killing.

Earl Boethar was on Rannerdale Ridge directing the battle beneath him, and very soon he launched his final weapon against the Normans. This consisted of a crowd of wild berserkers, who rushed down the slopes to where the confusion was greatest, and made particularly for the horses of the great Norman knights. These berserkers were half drunken with some spirit which made them impervious to pain; they were fleet of foot and lightly armed, and wherever they could they slipped in and made for the big horses, which they disembowelled as they passed beneath their bellies.

Their reckless bravery helped the terror which spread amongst the Frenchmen as they tried to get out of the valley, and finally a panic seized them. *"Sauve qui peut"*, was the cry, and their power of resistance was at an end.

Thousands flung themselves upon Earl Ackin's barrier of men, who in an orgy of killing were pressed back foot by foot. Their weapons were blunted, their strength was worn away, and at last the line began to break.

Some berserker got under the horses of Ranulf himself and his companions, and slashed them as he passed. Down they went, and the great noble tasted the terrors of meaner men. Some faithful servitor helped him up, and a subordinate gave up his horse to him. Ranulf had no idea now but to save himself; he got out of the press, avoided the men on foot, and galloped to Lorton, then made his way to

Cockermouth and to disgrace.

Thus ended the last attempt that was made to conquer Earl Boethar, and Lakeland remained at peace until King Stephen, long afterwards, ceded it to Scotland, with Carlisle and the Eden valley, and the country up to Alston, where there were silver mines.

Ranulf Meschin lived under a cloud until 1120, when he was allowed to succeed a relative as Earl of Chester; for he had friends and connections at Court, and there were many who did not blame him over much for having failed to subjugate the men of the mountains.

CHAPTER XIV

CONCLUSION

The victory of Rannerdale was magnificent, but Earl Ackin was among the dead. His body lay where the little church was subsequently built *in memento mori* by the monks of Carlisle long afterwards, but Ackin was carried to the spot from which he had engineered the battle in the Vale of Newlands, in accordance with his own wish; and the hill has ever since been called Ackin's Howe. The chapel in Rannerdale was no more than a chantry 18ft. by 30ft., but it was in use until 1735, and can still be traced. (See *Transactions* of the Cumberland and Westmorland Antiquarian Society, 1929).

It was hopeless to try to bury the great piles of Norman dead, but, as usual, they were systematically stripped, for clothing was scarce, and arms and armour were worth good money.

The English dead were conveyed (mostly by water) to the Long Howe, which was opened on the low hill behind Earl Boethar's manor house, and to the Nether Howe on the lake; but Ackin's body lay all night in the centre of the great house, coffined and surrounded by candles. At day break it was fastened on a horse's back, and those who loved him best made a procession past the mill and up the long Hause to the left, where there is now a road; then from the top of the hill, along the ridge to the left again, until they came to the place where the soil was deep enough for a grave. Here the priest from Gatesgarth read the dignified and comforting words with which the living part from their best beloved dead, and leave them to the wind and rain for ever.

It was a heavy task to bury those who had been killed at Brackenthwaite, for their numbers were great. But it was not meet and right to let Englishmen lie and rot like Norman invaders, and despite everything six or eight great burial places were dug out and the labour of love was resolutely performed.

There was a superstition that the spirits of the unburied dead wandered about the earth and lingered round their homes until the living performed this last service for them, and therefore fear as well as love would hurry the digging of graves.

A contemporary story told how the crew of a vessel cast away upon a rocky coast had gathered together in their native village each evening at dusk; and, without saying anything or answering questions, had slowly walked to the manor house, two of the men being sons of the owner. Here they sat silently night after night at a corner table by themselves, sad and melancholy, but making no sign.

Meanwhile the men of the village searched both East and West, until at last they found the wrecked ship, and the bodies lying here and there upon the shore. And when at last they were all decently buried, the ghosts came no more, but left the village in peace.

This is typical of the stories current among both Norwegians and English in the eleventh and twelfth centuries. Many such were recorded by Snorro Sturlason about 1140; but it is evident that no reasons of this sort applied to dead enemies, and it was the usual rule to leave them unburied, in order to deter and discourage any other army which might advance by the same route. In the case of small detachments killed in an ambuscade the bodies were, however, put out of sight, so as to convey no warning to any of their friends who might follow them.

Rannerdale valley was like a charnel house, but in the course of time the birds and beasts, the insects and worms, all did their appointed work, and to-day you can only say that there are more bluebells there than anywhere else, and perhaps there may be something in Omar Khyyám's idea that the loveliest flowers may spring from some dead Caesar's breast.

It remains a forgotten corner of the world, a solitude profound; no real road was ever made through it, and there are few paths. Its curious earthworks and zig-zags troubled generation after generation of farmers; but had it not been for the memorial chapel its story would have been long ago forgotten.

The graceful head of Whiteless Pike looks down upon it, and the ruddy sides of Grassmoor seem stupendous. They face Rannerdale Ridge, a pleasant walk from Buttermere with a few hundred feet of easy climbing. From here one gets the finest views of the neighbourhood and the most beautiful sunsets. Sometimes artists are struck by the sheer beauty of the hills; but since a good road was blasted round the rocky point, all the world leaves the battlefield on one side and hurries along towards the good cheer for which Buttermere is famous.

After the defeat of Ranulf le Meschin and the King's army, Earl Boethar marched to Ambleside and promptly converted the great *castrum* with its new fortifications into a heap of ruins, so that ever since it has been called "The Borrans", which has that meaning. The garrison retreated to Kendal, where the Normans were well content to be allowed to keep the road open to and from Carlisle, without troubling Lakeland again.

Eventually Earl Boethar reoccupied his ancestral home in Eskdale and made terms with William

Meschin about access to the port of Ravenglass; for William had learned that the King intended to make no further effort to conquer the rebels; hence he thought it wisest to be neighbourly and make friends with them.

Thus it came about that Boethar built himself a new house, a couple of miles below the old one at Butterikeld, and lived there in peace. Eventually he died and was buried close at hand, where a long barrow covers the bones of an earlier generation of warriors. The village round his house retained his name in its Norman form of Boet or Boot.

. . . .

In 1136 the counties of Cumberland and West-marieland were ceded by King Stephen to King David of Scotland, so that Boethar's people were no longer "rebels", and "Gille the son of Boet" ruled the earldom to the end of his life. (The Lakeland men fought on the Scottish side against the English at the Battle of the Standard, near Northallerton, and were defeated by Bishop Thurston.)

Buttermere is almost the only place in England which was never subject to any of the four Norman Kings, and those who examine its natural defences will realise that it was a very wonderful stronghold. The stately pass from Honister is too obviously a death-trap for any army to have tried to march through it in wartime, and the boggy valley called Mosedale is impracticable even now, except in times of drought, and its only attraction is the great waterfall of Scale Force.

King David and his son Henry both died in 1153, and as our King Henry II pressed for the two counties to be given back, they were retroceded by Malcolm the Maiden in 1158, and Carlisle was peaceably reoccupied by the King of England.

The position of "Gille the son of Boet" was fully acknowledged, and he is mentioned many times in documents of King Henry II, so that it is probable his people lived in peace and in greater freedom than the rest of England. As the years rolled on the descendants of the refugees drifted towards their old homes, and the Lakeland population diminished to the number which its agriculture could most easily support. The bravery and generalship of the great Earl Boethar and his generation had saved a section of our race from extermination, and it is not surprising that even to this day many of us make an instinctive yearly pilgrimage to Lakeland, conscious that we owe something to the mountains, and that from them alone the very best that is in us can draw strength and inspiration.

NOTA BENE

The reason why no Lake Country Saga has survived is not far to seek. The only person who had sufficient culture and leisure to write one out would be a monk who was not above associating with the people; and the monks were either Norman or leaned to the Norman party then in power, who regarded all Englishmen as barbarians; and not only made little distinction between Norse, Angle, and Welsh, but knew little and cared less for their history and beliefs.

Dr. C. A. Parker in the foreword to *The Story of Shelagh, Olaf Cuarar's Daughter.*

. . . .

Dunmail, son of Donal and grand-nephew of Constantine. Last king of Strathclyde 937 to 945. He seems to have had power in Wales after his defeat, and died on a pilgrimage to Rome. --- *Wendover and Ulster Annals.*

The poems of Wordsworth and John Pagen White on this subject are noted and disregarded as they are not reliable.

. . . .

The name of Meschin or Le Meschin means Junior in Norman French, and Ranulf and William were members of the family of De Briscasard of Bayeux in Normandy.

In 1092 William Rufus set up Walter the Priest to rebuild Carlisle, and gave the custody of the district to Ranulf Meschin. He then returned *via* Appleby and Middleham Castle, carefully avoiding the Lake District.

. . . .

The "Testa de Nevill" shows that in the reign of Henry I Ranulf Meschin appointed Barons to represent him on the Scottish Border near the Solway and in Mardale &c.

The *Victoria History* says, on page 306, "It is not disputed that the family of Bueth or Boet held its own against the Norman intruder, both when Ranulf was in possession of Carlisle, and also when Henry I took over possession of it on Ranulf's succession to Hugh, Earl of Chester".

. . . .

Gille was eventually murdered by Hubert de Vallibus at an arbitration meeting arranged by the Church near Lanercost, and the Priory is said to have been built as an act of atonement. In consequence of this murder Henry II granted a deed securing all Lakeland to the family of "Gille the son of Boet" for ever; but subsequently revoked it at

Newcastle, thus justifying the wisdom of those who put not their trust in Princes.

The bargain granting the men of Cumberland and Westmarieland immunity from military service is the subject of an article in the *Scottish* Antiquary, xvii, 105/11. In the original deed it was agreed that they should safely convoy the King's armies through their counties, marching in the van from the Rerecross on Stainmoor to Scotland, and in the rear on the return journey.

. . . .

The following is a copy of the grant of land by Henry II to Robert de Vallibus, son of Hubert de Vallibus, the murderer of Gille: "Totam terram quam Gillius filius Boet tenvit die qua fuit vivus et mortuus de quocunque illam tenuissit. --- Carte antiquae No 7 in Chancery".

In this deed Robert is granted all the lands of which his father's victim was possessed on the day when he was murdered --- or as it is mildly put --- "the day upon which he was both living and dead". Thus was the son of the murderer rewarded; and the Church --- which had made itself responsible for the safety of Earl Gille --- contented itself by demanding something for its own benefit as an act of atonement for flouting its authority.

. . . .

The lands of Earl Gille stretched eastward to Alston, in Northumberland, where there were the richest silver mines in the British Isles, and if the Scottish had retained the rugged province ceded to them by King Stephen it might have altered their history, for though the Alston mines yield little except lead at present, a fabulous wealth of silver has come out of them.

. . . . . .

Early in 1929, the author and other members of the Cumberland and Westmorland Antiquarian Society actually came within touch of those remote days when Gille the son of Boethar was Earl, and Cumberland and Westmorland were part of Scotland. A question arose about a cross on Hartside of which there was no trace, and it occurred to one member that nobody would try to make a cross out of the Hartside stone when decent sandstone could be obtained a few miles away. Three enthusiasts at once volunteered to search every yard of Hartside for some remaining scrap of sandstone, hoping it would indicate the locality of the ancient cross.

At last they came upon a piece of stone no larger than a man's fist which upon investigation widened out to a square shaft. They raised this stone to see if anything had been buried at the base in accordance with the ancient custom, and found a coin which had lain at the base for 800 years. A silver penny blackened with age, a beautiful piece of money, coined by Alexander III, King of Scotland, and placed there after King Stephen ceded the country to the Scots.

.   .   .   .

And so my story ends --- a story no less interesting for being substantially true. It consists of little more than our local history, with some of the events explained in detail, and here and there an imaginary conversation designed to show what was going on. Jackson the Herder never existed; he is merely the type of an ignorant and credulous spy, whose information, given in all good faith, merely injured his employer. There were many such from before the days when King Alfred spied for himself and played the harp in the camp of his enemies, right down to the Great War of 1914; and no doubt spies always will exist whether there is money in the business or not.

Some of my friends have criticised me for not writing a colourless account of my facts, with every reference carefully recorded; but such a book would have been nearly as dry as dust, and few people would trouble to read it. Surely this modern method will go further because it is easier and more attractive.

The great Dr. Johnson says that "No good story is ever wholly true", and people do not expect it. There are details to imagine, and suggestions to make in order to cover points which have not been recorded; and as life is too short for most of us, it seems best to put the facts into the form of a readable story appreciated by the many, instead of into a dry handbook appreciated by the very few.

DEDICATED
TO THE MEMORY OF
BRAITHWAITE RIGG
STONE WALLER, ROAD MENDER,
AND LOCAL HISTORIAN, KINDEST AND
MOST CONTENTED OF NATURE'S
GENTLEMEN WHOSE HANDIWORK
REMAINS IN MANY A WALL AT
BUTTERMERE, AND WHOSE
TRADITIONS OF THE PLACE
MAY YET LIVE FOR AS
LONG AS THE VERY
STONES WHICH HE
KNEW SO WELL
HOW TO
HANDLE

Nicholas Size,
June, 1930.

Other books published by Llanerch include:

LAYS AND LEGENDS OF THE ENGLISH LAKES,
J. Pagen White.

THORSTEIN OF THE MERE: A SAGA OF THE NORTHMEN IN
LAKELAND.
W. G. Collingwood.

THE BONDWOMEN: A SAGA OF THE NORTHMEN IN
LAKELAND (Sequel to Thorstein of the Mere),
W. G. Collingwood.

TALIESIN POEMS (including the verses to the northern king, Urien
of Rheged),
translated by Meirion Pennar.

DURCH AGNES: A JOURNAL OF THE CURATE OF CONISTON
1616-1623,
W. G. Collingwood.

THE LIKENESS OF KING ELFWALD: A STUDY OF IONA AND
NORTHUMBRIA DURING THE VIKING AGE,
W. G. Collingwood.

NORTHANHYMBRE SAGA: A HISTORY OF THE KINGS OF
NORTHUMBRIA,
John Marsden.

LAKELAND AND ICELAND: THE LANDNAMA BOOK OF ICELAND
& A GLOSSARY OF WORDS IN THE DIALECT OF
CUMBERLAND ETC.,
T. Ellwood.

For a complete list of c.200 titles, small-press editions & facsimile
reprints, write to LLANERCH PUBLISHERS, FELINFACH,
LAMPETER, DYFED, SA48 8PJ.